Nearing the planet Eminiar VII, the crew of the Starship *Enterprise* picks up a message coded 710, clearly warning them that under NO CIRCUMSTANCES should they continue their approach. But an overzealous Federation Ambassador orders Captain Kirk to disregard the message and beam down to the planet's surface.

There, Kirk and his landing party are held captive and find themselves unwilling participants in an intergalactic war that the Eminians have been fighting for nearly 500 years. A war unlike any other. A war with battles, but no blood. A war with death, but no killings. Where not a single shot is fired, yet casualties number in the millions. A war without destruction, yet thousands are destroyed.

It all seems some kind of incredible game until the Starship itself becomes a vulnerable target caught between the two beligerent enemies and Kirk's only chance to save his entire crew gives him much more than...

**A TASTE
OF ARMAGEDDON**

OTHER **STAR TREK FOTONOVELS**™
YOU WILL ENJOY—

THE CITY ON THE
EDGE OF FOREVER

WHERE NO MAN
HAS GONE BEFORE

THE TROUBLE
WITH TRIBBLES

STAR TREK ™*

A TASTE OF ARMAGEDDON

written by **ROBERT HAMNER**
and **GENE L. COON**

adapted from the television series
created by **GENE RODDENBERRY**

A TASTE OF ARMAGEDDON
A Bantam Book / January 1978

Star Trek™ *designates a trademark of
Paramount Pictures Corporation.*

Fotonovel™ *designates a trademark of
Mandala Productions.*

ISBN 0-553-11348-8

Published simultaneously in the United States and Canada

PRINTED IN THE UNITED STATES OF AMERICA

0 9 8 7 6 5 4 3 2 1

CONVERSATION WITH SCOTTY (CONT'D.)

by Caryl Eagle

The first part of this interview with **James Doohan,** *a.k.a. Scotty of the Starship* Enterprise, *was printed in* The Trouble With Tribbles. *The conclusion follows:*

C.E.: What are the Star Trek conventions like?

J.D.: They're fantastic! The fans are so warm. I am proud to be a part of Star Trek. It's funny, if I meet someone who doesn't recognize me, I always say I'm a Space Technologist.

C.E.: How did you get involved in Star Trek in the first place?

J.D.: The producer remembered me from a reading I had done the week before. I turned out to be too young for that part but I was just the right age for the Chief Engineer on the Starship. They had me read the part in five different dialects and eventually settled on the Scotch accent. I actually chose the character's name myself. I picked Montgomery because it was my mother's maiden name and Scott...well, that's sort of obvious.

C.E.: Had you not played Scott, what other character on the Starship appeals to you?

J.D.: Why, Captain, of course! There's so much diversity in the role. Scotty rarely gets off the bridge, but the Captain goes everywhere...does everything. For an actor, the part offers more.

C.E.: When did you know you had a winner?

J.D.: When I read the scripts. It's a classic. It's appeal just goes on and on and seems to only grow stronger. As proof, look at your own Fotonovels. Why would you choose Star Trek to launch this series of books? You yourselves must have recognized its wide appeal.

C.E.: We certainly did.

J.D.: Scott out!

CAST LIST

James T. Kirk, Captain
William Shatner

A man in his mid 30's whose independent nature and compassionate heart make him a natural leader. His overriding concern is always the well-being of his ship and crew.

Spock, First Officer
Leonard Nimoy

Chief Science Officer. Of Vulcan heritage, which accounts for his analytical mind and extraordinary strength. His life is almost totally ruled by reason and logic.

Leonard McCoy, M.D.,
Lt. Commander
DeForest Kelley

Though surrounded by the most advanced equipment the 24th century can offer, he still practices medicine more with his heart than with his head.

Montgomery Scott,
Lt. Commander
James Doohan

Chief Engineer. A middle-aged man of Scottish descent whose knowledge of the ship's engineering section is boundless.

Ambassador Robert Fox
Gene Lyons

Special Representative to Eminiar VII, who finally learns that in some instances, diplomacy is not the only answer.

Anan-7
David Opatoshu
Head Councilman of the Eminian Union. For the first time in 500 years, he has the opportunity to bring his people peace, not war.

Mea-3
Barbara Babcock
An Official of the Eminian Union. Her high consciousness of duty stops at nothing, even if it means her own death.

Uhura
Lt. Communications Officer
Nichelle Nichols

Sar-6
Anan-7's Assistant
Robert Sampson

Yeoman Tamura
Miko Mayama

Lt. De Paul
Sean Kenney

Lt. Galloway
David L. Ross

Eminians Guards & Technicians

Bill Blackburn
John Burnside
Eddie Paskey
Ron Veto
Frank Vinci

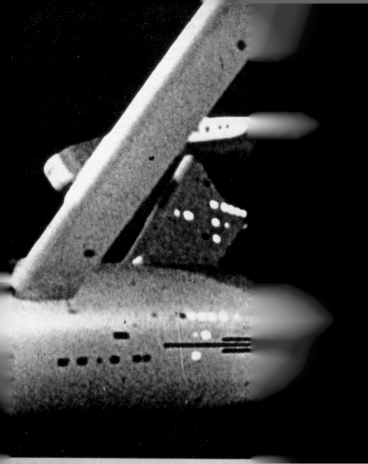

SPACE:

THE FINAL FRONTIER

THESE ARE THE VOYAGES OF
THE STARSHIP "ENTERPRISE."
ITS FIVE YEAR MISSION: TO
EXPLORE STRANGE NEW
WORLDS...TO SEEK OUT NEW
LIFE AND NEW CIVILIZATIONS
...TO BOLDLY GO WHERE NO
MAN HAS GONE BEFORE.

A TASTE OF ARMAGEDDON

CAPTAIN'S LOG:

STARDATE 3192.1

THE "ENTERPRISE" IS ON
ROUTE TO STAR CLUSTER
N.G.C. 321.
OBJECTIVE: TO OPEN
DIPLOMATIC RELATIONS
WITH THE CIVILIZA-
TIONS KNOWN TO BE
THERE. WE HAVE SENT
A MESSAGE TO EMINIAR
VII, PRINCIPAL
PLANET OF THE STAR
CLUSTER, INFORMING
THEM OF OUR FRIENDLY
INTENTIONS. WE ARE
AWAITING AN ANSWER.

An anxious Captain is keeping a watchful eye over the Communicator's post.

Anything yet, Lieutenant?

Nothing, Captain, but the hailing frequencies are open.

While Kirk attends to his various duties on the bridge, he is joined by Robert Fox, the Federation's Ambassador assigned to open diplomatic relations with Eminiar VII. The Ambassador takes his responsibility **very seriously** and it is quite clear that he will allow **no one** or **no thing** to stand in the way of accomplishing his mission—**including** Captain Kirk.

Have you received an answer to your message yet, Captain?

Nothing so far, Ambassador. We're awaiting a reply now. But you must remember that today is the first time we've had any evidence that they've picked up our signal.

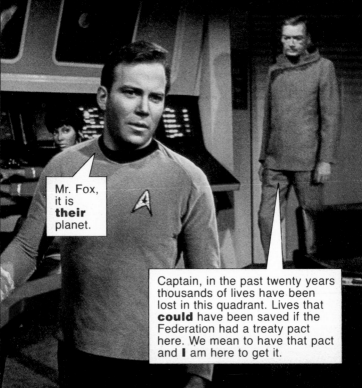

We're going in gentlemen. Peacefully I hope, but peacefully or not...**we're going in.**

CAPTAIN'S LOG:

STARDATE 3192.5

NOW IN STANDARD ORBIT AROUND PLANET EMINIAR VII. MY ORDERS ARE CLEAR. WE MUST ESTABLISH DIPLOMATIC RELATIONS AT ALL COSTS. PREPARING TO BEAM DOWN TO THE PLANET'S SURFACE.

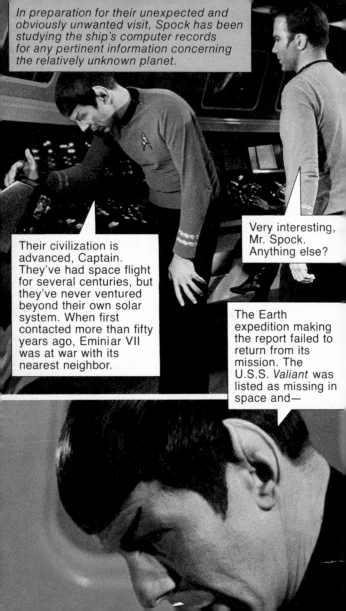

Moments later, the Starship's landing party materializes on the planet's surface.

I see our arrival has not gone unnoticed. **Be on your guard.**

I know. I congratulate you on your instrumentation, Captain. You've come directly to the Division of Control. You'll follow me, please. Anan-7 and the members of the High Council await you.

The landing party is led into the adjacent building and down various corridors, but before entering the Council Room, Mea stops. There is a question that she feels she must ask...

Why have you come here, Captain? You were **warned** not to.

The danger exists. Nevertheless, you are here. It would be morally incorrect to do less than extend our hospitality. Now, if you'll come this way...

A few moments later, the landing party is ushered into the Council Room.

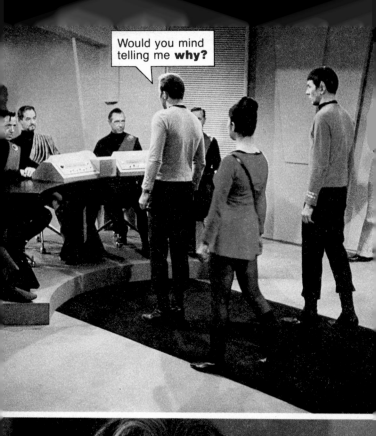

Have the Scanners picked up anything unusual on the planet's surface?
Nothing, sir. All quiet.
Thank you. Kirk out.
While Kirk and his landing party try to put the pieces of this confusing puzzle together, Anan and his top aide, Sar, are concentrating on the business of war.
Look, Councilman.
Yes, I see it. But, they **were** warned.

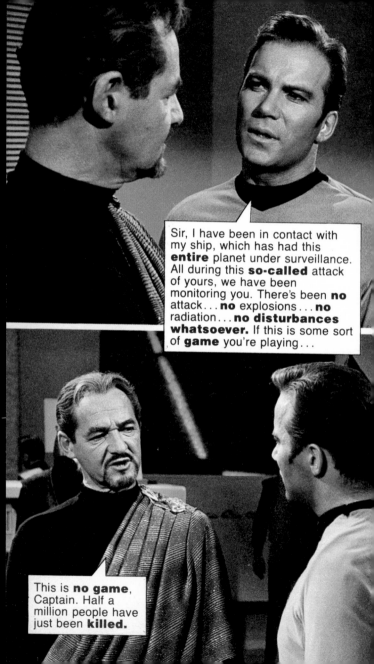

Then the attack by Vendikar was theoretical?

Oh, no, **quite real.** An attack is mathematically launched. I lost my wife in the last one. Our civilization lives, the people die, but our culture goes on.

The bizarreness of the whole situation is almost too much for Kirk to comprehend.

You mean to tell me your people just **walk** into a disintegration machine when they're **told** to?

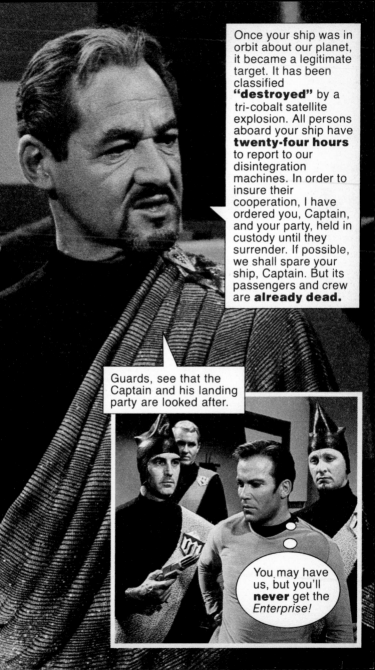

DELAYED ENTRY

THE "ENTERPRISE," IN ORBIT ABOUT EMINIAR VII, HAS BEEN DECLARED A CASUALTY OF AN INCREDIBLE WAR FOUGHT BY COMPUTERS.

MY LANDING PARTY AND I, THOUGH APPARENTLY NOT INCLUDED AS CASUALTIES ABOARD THE "ENTERPRISE," ARE CONFINED ON THE PLANET'S SUR- FACE, AWAITING ...WHAT?

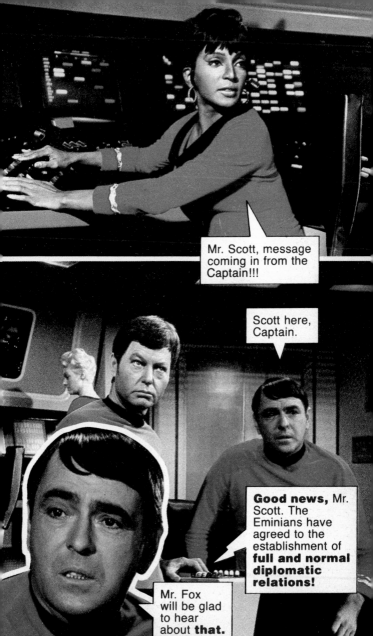

He certainly would be **if** the voice they were hearing was actually Kirk's. But it is **not.** It is **Anan's,** being filtered through a sophisticated voice duplicator.

They've also extended an invitation to all personnel to come down for shore leave. They've assured me that our people will have a **wonderful** time.

Something doesn't quite sit right in the minds of Scott and McCoy. They have been awaiting word from the Captain, and it has come. Why aren't they pleased? Somehow they can't shake the thought that something is **dreadfully wrong.** But what?

Well now, what do you think of **that?**

I don't know... I don't know.

But **I** do.

I canna quite buy the bit about **"all personnel"** transporting down.

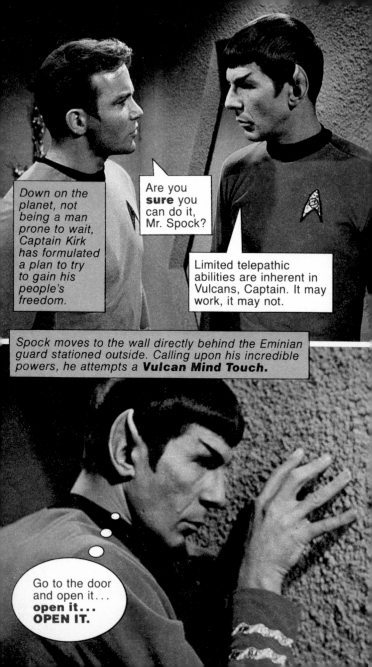

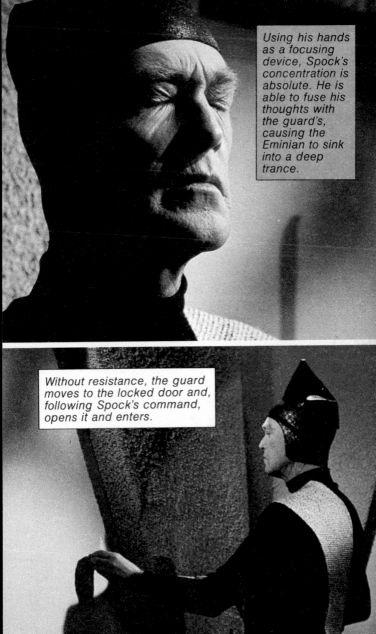

Using his hands as a focusing device, Spock's concentration is absolute. He is able to fuse his thoughts with the guard's, causing the Eminian to sink into a deep trance.

Without resistance, the guard moves to the locked door and, following Spock's command, opens it and enters.

O.K. Let's go. Everyone, **stay alert!**

Cautiously the group slips out of the room...

...and inches its way down the long, unfamiliar corridors, not sure of their destination but spurred on by their knowledge that the fate of the Starship and its entire crew depends upon their actions.

Peering around a corner, the group spots several Eminians gathered at the other end of the hallway. Retreating into the relative safety of the shadows, they watch as a young woman quietly steps into a raised chamber...

...and a guard posted nearby silently pushes a button that closes the door.

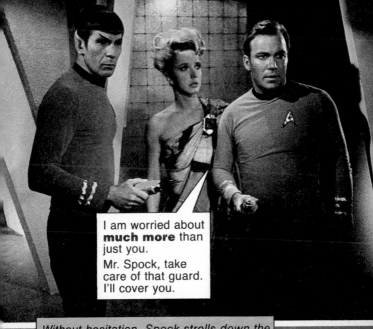

I am worried about **much more** than just you.
Mr. Spock, take care of that guard. I'll cover you.

Without hesitation, Spock strolls down the corridor and approaches the group of Eminians.

I think this calls for a little **Vulcan** ingenuity.

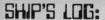

SHIP'S LOG:

STARDATE 3193.0

CHIEF ENGINEER SCOTT RECORDING.
THE CAPTAIN AND FIRST OFFICER
ARE OVERDUE AND MISSING ON THE
SURFACE OF EMINIAR VII. I HAVE
TAKEN STANDARD PRECAUTIONARY
MEASURES WHILE WE CONTINUE OUR
ATTEMPTS TO LOCATE THEM.

All stations reporting. Deflector screens rigged at full power. Phaser crews ready. Sensors reading zero... Correction, Mr. Scott. You better see this for yourself.

Sensor readings just shot **off the scale!**

They're taking **pot shots** at us! Are the screens holding?

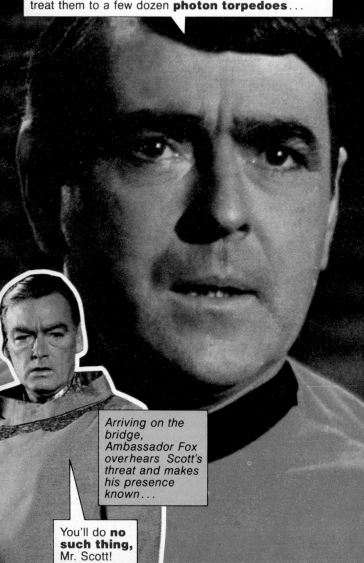

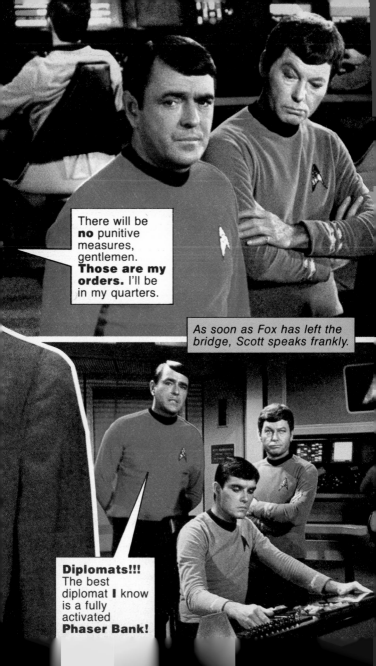

*Meanwhile, back on the planet, Kirk and the others have returned to the room where they had been held captives. Kirk has figured correctly that it is the **last** place the Eminians would look for them.*

We'll stay here for awhile. Yeoman, cover the door.

Yes, sir.

Captain Kirk, you have **got** to let me go. My time is almost up.

Are you **that** anxious to die?

You just don't understand...

*Mea is absolutely right. Kirk does **not** understand. He cannot comprehend how anyone could accept their death so willingly. His whole being **rebels** at the very idea and he is convinced that there must be some way to bring Mea to her senses.*

*Time is **definitely** running out.*

Fellow Councilmen, we have been **unable** to destroy the Earth ship. One of our disintegration chambers has been eliminated and we have already fallen **far below** our quota. This is a **grave crisis** and I am at a loss to know how to proceed. Which is the greatest morality? Open honesty, or a deception which **may** save our lives?

Knowing that his planet's very existence rests in his hands, Anan makes the exceedingly difficult decision.

Put me through to the Earth Ambassador.

I'm sure that from this day forward your planet and our Federation will attain the **deepest friendship**. I look forward to seeing you.

But the moment the communicator is switched off, Anan drops the pose of gracious statesman and reveals his true intentions.

The minute their screens are down, **open fire**, Sar. This time we've **got** them!

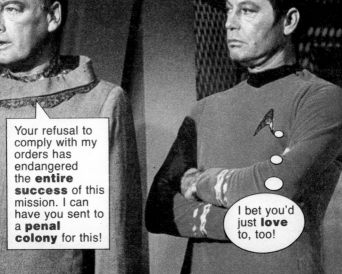

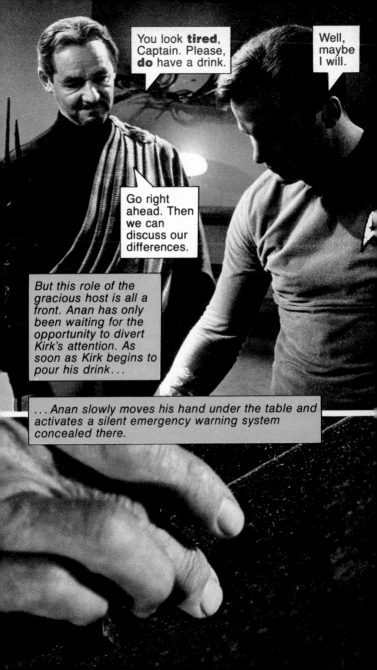

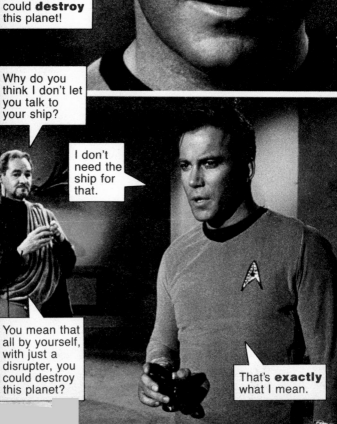

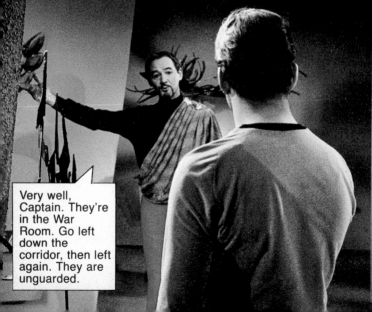

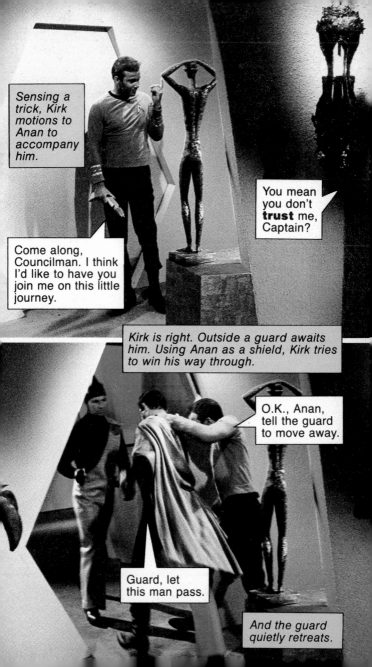

I beg your pardon?

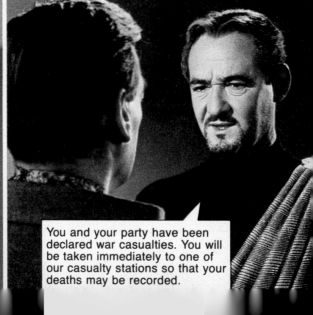

You and your party have been declared war casualties. You will be taken immediately to one of our casualty stations so that your deaths may be recorded.

Just as the Ambassador is being shoved into the disintegration chamber, Spock, accompanied by his two fellow crewmen disguised in their Eminian uniforms, appears at the other end of the corridor.

Who goes there?

Another casualty.

Before the real Eminian guards can spot the imposters, Spock and his men make their move, quickly overpower the guards, and take their weapons.

As soon as everyone has moved back...
What are you doing, Mr. Spock?
Practicing a peculiar variety of diplomacy, sir.

And they all witness the end of the machinery that has itself ended so many lives.

As the smoke clears...

I'll take you to a place of comparative safety. Then I must find the Captain.

They have him. The guards told us. They took him to the Council Room, under heavy guard.

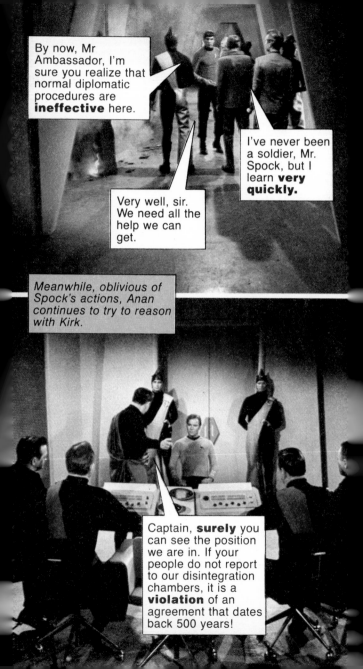

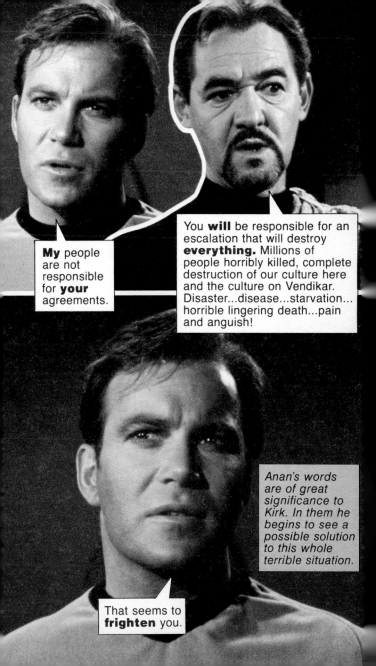

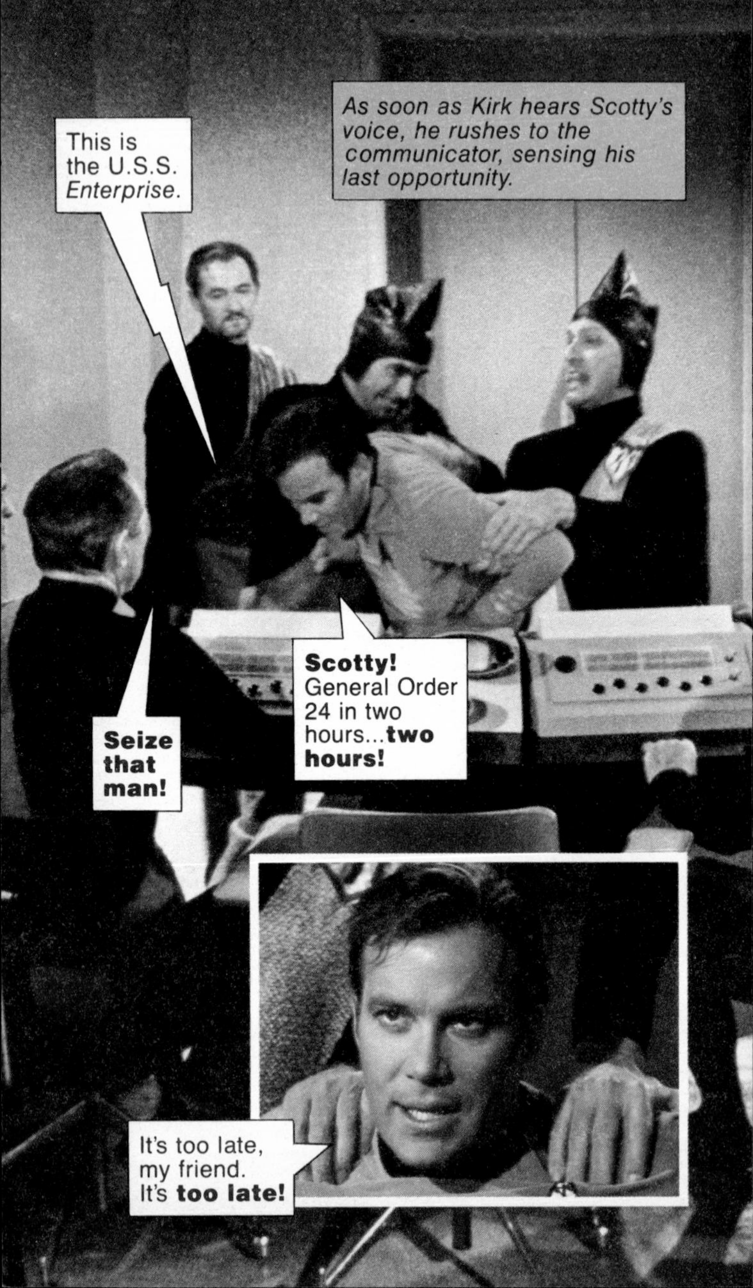
As soon as Kirk hears Scotty's voice, he rushes to the communicator, sensing his last opportunity.
This is the U.S.S. Enterprise.
Scotty! General Order 24 in two hours...two hours!
Seize that man!
It's too late, my friend. It's too late!

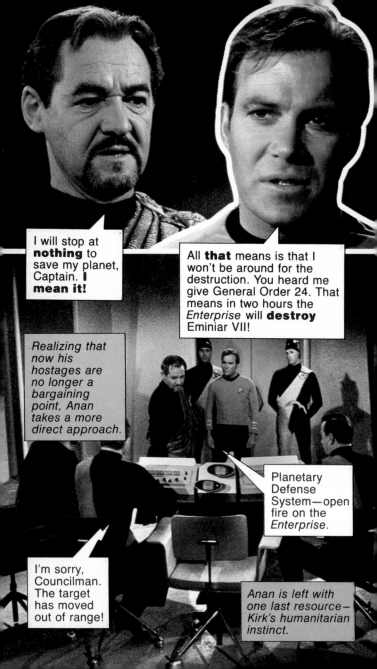

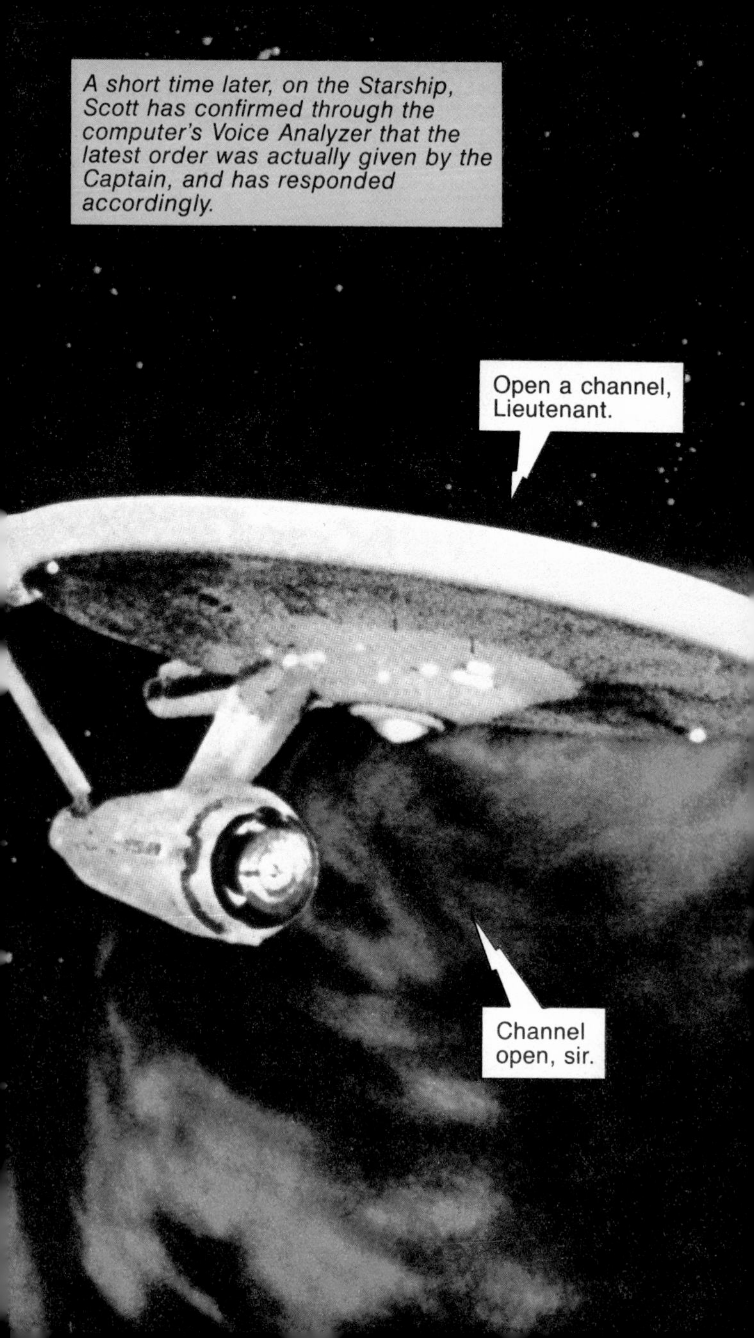
A short time later, on the Starship, Scott has confirmed through the computer's Voice Analyzer that the latest order was actually given by the Captain, and has responded accordingly.
Open a channel, Lieutenant.
Channel open, sir.

Just then, Spock and his men burst into the room.

Captain, we're— Oh...I had assumed you needed **help**. I see I'm in **error**.

No, I **do** need your help. **In there**, Mr. Spock.

With General Order 24 just minutes away, Kirk makes his last attempt at saving not only his own life and his people's, but those of the whole Eminian Empire.

Death, destruction, disease, horror. **That's** what war is all about, Anan. That's what makes it a thing to be avoided. You've made it **neat** and **painless.** So neat and painless you've had no reason to **stop** it. And you've had it for 500 years.

The moment the room is cleared, Kirk aims his phaser and fires.

*The computer explodes in flames. But **how** will this stop the war? It will merely stop the Eminian's ability to fight. How will it stop the Vendikans? What could Kirk have in mind? He has just pronounced Eminiar's death sentence! Or **has** he?*

They had been killing three million people a year for almost 500 years. An **actual** attack wouldn't have killed any more people than their computer attacks. But it would have ended their **ability** to make war. The fighting would have been over permanently.

But you didn't know that it would work.

GLOSSARY

Armageddon—A final conclusive battle between the forces of good and evil as foretold in the New Testament.

Code 710—A signal warning the receiver that under no circumstances whatsoever should the sender be approached.

Disintegration Chambers—Small compartments located throughout Eminiar VII used to eliminate bodies in order to satisfy casualty requirements.

Disrupter—Personal weapon similar to the Federation's phaser, but more limited in power.

Eminiar VII—Chief planet of star cluster NGC 321.

Deflector Screens—Main defense system utilized by a Starship, capable of protecting it from contact with hostile matter. They are automatically activated whenever the ship is threatened, but can also be manually operated.

General Order 24—A command directing the receiver to destroy the designated target after the time specified unless the order is specifically revoked.

Phasers—Personal weapons with adjustable settings ranging from heat activator to kill.

Photon Torpedo—Self-propelled missile with great destructive powers capable of speeds of several warp factors.

Ship's Log—Record keeping method of all activities aboard a starship. Entries are made by the Captain or, in his absence, the next in command.

Transporter—Used to move crew and/or cargo from a starship to planets and back by changing the object's original molecular structure into energy which is beamed to a predetermined point where the original molecular formation is reconstructed.

Tricorder—Portable, miniaturized computer, capable of recording, analyzing and identifying all matter.

United Federation of Planets—Democratic alliance of planets comprised of several star systems including Sol.

Vendikar—The third planet in star cluster NGC 321 and the one closest to Eminiar VII. Though now their ruthless enemy, it was originally settled by the Eminians themselves.

Voice Analyzer—A sub-function of the computer which determines the authenticity of voice communications.

Voice Duplicator— A mechanical contrivance capable of imitating the pronunciation, inflection and accent of anyone's speech so closely that the human ear cannot detect the falsification.

Vulcan Mind Touch— A form of non-verbal communication passed from one mind to another, perfected by Vulcans.

Vulcan Nerve Pinch—a method of temporarily immobilizing one's victim requiring knowledge of anatomy.

STAR TREK QUIZ #4

In each question below, circle the one answer that best completes the sentence.

1. A message coded 710 means:
   a. emergency help needed
   b. stay away
   c. welcome, come down.
   d. phaser crews standing by.

2. After being captured by the Eminians, Kirk is unable to contact the _Enterprise_ because:
   a. his communicator doesn't work on the planet
   b. he is constantly guarded
   c. the Starship cannot receive messages while its deflector screens are up
   d. his communicator is taken away from him

3. In their attacks, the Vendikans use:
   a. imaginary fusion bombs
   b. anti-cobalt satellite explosions
   c. photon torpedoes
   d. disrupter beams

4. Ambassador Fox is anxious to get to his destination so that he can:
   a. put an end to the war
   b. exchange technological information
   c. arrange for a treaty pact
   d. open up diplomatic relations with Vendikar

5. Anan explains that his planet used disrupter beams against the Starship because:
   a. Kirk refused to cooperate
   b. the Vendikans knocked out their tracking system
   c. of an error in their sensors
   d. their message coded 710 was ignored

6. Trova is:

   a. an uncharted planet in the N.G.C. star cluster
   b. a liquid refreshment
   c. the governing body of Eminiar VII
   d. Sar's assistant

7. The Eminians utilize computers in fighting their war because:

   a. it minimizes the number of casualties
   b. they have no standing army
   c. it's less costly than normal weapons
   d. it stops their civilization from being destroyed

8. Scott becomes suspicious that the message he receives might not be from Captain Kirk when he hears that:

   a. the Starship's crew will have a wonderful time
   b. the Eminians will transport up trained personnel to run the Starship
   c. the Eminians have agreed to the establishment of full normal diplomatic relations
   d. all Starship personnel should beam down

9. The Federation first made contact with the Eminians:

   a. 50 years before
   b. when the U.S.S. *Valiant* made an emergency landing there
   c. after the Vendikans joined the Federation
   d. when Ambassador Fox ordered Captain Kirk to go down to the planet

10. Scott refuses to lower the deflector screens until:

   a. Captain Kirk tells him to
   b. the Eminians stop their attack
   c. he is sure that Anan is not lying again
   d. Ambassador Fox threatens to send him to a penal colony

Turn the page for the answers.